This book belongs to:

_____

# Contents

Cover illustration by Peter Stevenson

Published by Ladybird Books Ltd
27 Wrights Lane  London  W8 5TZ
A Penguin Company

2 4 6 8 10 9 7 5 3

© LADYBIRD BOOKS LTD MCMXCVII, MMI

# Seaside surprise

written by Marie Birkinshaw
illustrated by Julie Anderson

"Can **I** have the big spade
now?" asked Anna.

"Here," said Matthew,
"but I'll need it again soon."

They were racing to make
a giant sandcastle before
the tide came in.

"Look, Dad! We've done it!"
they shouted.

When the sea came up to them,
they all ran to the rocks.

They watched sadly as
the water flowed round
the castle walls.
Soon there was nothing left.

Suddenly they spotted
something in the water.

"Oh, no!" Anna shouted.
"We've left the big spade
behind."

"It's too late to get it now,"
Matthew said.

"We'll get it in the
morning," said Dad.

Next day they looked
everywhere. The tide was
a really long way out and
they found lots of interesting
things in the rock pools.

Dad showed them some
sea-snails, periwinkles,
barnacles and dogwhelks.
But they couldn't see
the spade.

sea-snail

barnacle

dogwhelk

periwinkle

11

Anna, Matthew and Dad walked by some fishing boats.

"Look!" said Matthew. "That fisherman has a spade just like the one we lost in the sea."

"It's not mine!" said the fisherman. "We found it in the nets last night. It must be yours. Would you like it back?"

"Oh, yes, please!" said Anna.

"Thanks a lot!" shouted Matthew. "Come on, Anna! We've got just enough time to make another sandcastle before the tide comes in."

"But we'll bring the spade back this time," smiled Anna.

# Seashore Facts

- The sea rises up the shore twice a day, and then goes back down again. When the sea comes up the shore, this is called **high tide**. When it has gone back down again, this is called **low tide**. There are approximately six hours between high tide and low tide.

- Rock pools are formed when the tide goes out. Water is left behind in puddles that are large enough for small creatures to live in.

- Many animals that live in rock pools are **camouflaged**. This means that, because of their colour and shape, they are difficult to see and so are protected from being eaten by other animals.

- **Limpets** return to exactly the same place on the rocks every time the tide goes out.

- Some beaches are pebbly and some are sandy. **Sand** is made of rocks and seashells that have been broken up by the sea into very small pieces. Black sand has either coal or volcanic rock in it. Sometimes, waves crash directly against cliffs, wearing them away to make caves and arches where the rock is soft.

- **Seaweed** has no roots, unlike a garden plant, but it can grip rocks so that it is not swept away by the sea. Some seaweed can survive out of water for a long time.

- The common prawn's favourite food is **sea lettuce**!

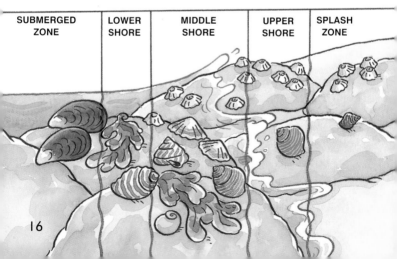

| SUBMERGED ZONE | LOWER SHORE | MIDDLE SHORE | UPPER SHORE | SPLASH ZONE |
|---|---|---|---|---|

# Down in the sea

written by Shirley Jackson
illustrated by Ilaria Matteini

Down in the sea,
where the seashells lie,

Six seahorses came
swimming by.

Down in the sea,
where the waters flow,

Six little mermaids
saw them go.

"I'll have the green one."
"I'll have the pink."
"I'll have the blue one.
What do you think?"

"I'll have the red one."
"The silver one's fine."
But the Sea Princess said,
"The gold one's mine."

So off they went through
the sunlit waves,

And raced in and out
of the watery caves.

At last, late at night,
they came to a rest.

And the Sea Princess said,

"The gold one's best!"

# The school photograph

written by Lorraine Horsley
illustrated by Peter Stevenson

"Say 'Cheese'," said the photographer.

Lucy Sanderson put up her hand.
"Please, Miss, Dennis Hill is
pulling my hair."

"Stop it at once, Dennis,"
said Mrs Taylor.

We all folded our arms and
smiled at the camera.

"Say 'Cheese'," said
the photographer.

Parul Patel put up her hand.
"Please, Miss, Dennis Hill is
pulling a funny face."

"Stop it at once, Dennis,"
said Mrs Taylor. "Please be
good or you'll have to sit
next to me."

We all folded our arms and
smiled at the camera.

"Say 'Cheese'," said
the photographer.

Our class photo came today.
Mrs Taylor says it's the
best ever.

Dennis Hill's mum thinks it's
great too.

"You look like the best boy in
the class," she said.

# New words

Encourage your child to use some of these words to
help her to write her own very simple stories and rhymes.
Go back to look at earlier books and their wordlists to
practise other words.

35

# Read with Ladybird

**Read with Ladybird** has been written to help you to help your child:

- to take the first steps in reading
- to improve early reading progress
- to gain confidence

## Main Features

- **Several stories and rhymes in each book**

This means that there is not too much for you and your child to read in one go.

- **Rhyme and rhythm**

**Read with Ladybird** uses rhymes or stories with a rhythm to help your child to predict and memorise new words.

- **Gradual introduction and repetition of key words**

**Read with Ladybird** introduces and repeats the 100 most frequently used words in the English language.

- **Compatible with school reading schemes**

The key words that your child will learn are compatible with the word lists that are used in schools. This means that you can be confident that practising at home will support work done at school.

- **Information pullout**

Use this pullout to understand more about how you can use each story to help your child to learn to read.

But the most important feature of **Read with Ladybird** is for you and your child to have fun sharing the stories and rhymes with each other.

# Learning to read with this book

## Seaside surprise

Be prepared to spend a little longer than ten minutes on this story and to enjoy listening as your child reads it to you.

If she hesitates at any of the words, wait for a few seconds before offering to help. She may be able to work the word out or to correct a mistaken reading for herself. When she's read the story, it's her turn to enjoy listening as you read the Seashore Facts to her.

## Down in the sea

Have a reading 'rehearsal' of this lovely rhyme. First, help your child with any words she cannot read. Then enjoy listening to her read this rhyme fluently.

## The school photograph

Show how much you enjoy hearing this story as your child reads it to you. Experiment with putting lots of expression into the voices of the children and the teacher!